my first rhyming picture abc

Written by Brian Miles
Illustrated by Anne and Ken McKie

Text © Brian Miles, 1985
Illustrations © Grandreams Ltd., 1985

© 1986 Modern Publishing, a division of Unisystems, Inc.,

PUBLISHED BY MODERN PUBLISHING
A Division of Unisystems, Inc.
New York, New York 10022

Printed in Singapore

A a

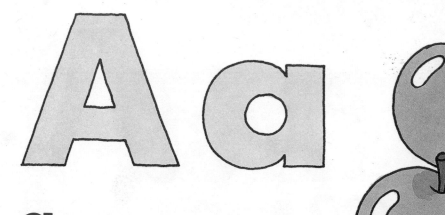

a is for apples
some green, some red

a is for airplane
that flies overhead

a is for apricot
that grows on a tree

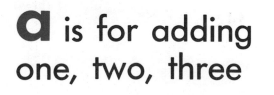

a is for adding
one, two, three

B b

b is for baker
who bakes crusty bread

b is for blanket
that covers your bed

b is for breakfast
you eat every day

b is for binoculars
to see far away

C c

C is for cat
with its whiskers long

C is for cart
pulled by a horse so strong

C is for carrot
crunchy and sweet

C is for cars
that you see in the street

D d

d is for dancing
so light on your feet

d is for drinking
orange juice so sweet

d is for dog
wagging his tail

d is for dinghy
with a bright blue sail

E e

e is for eggs
see the chicks that hatch out

e is for excitement
when we all laugh and shout

e is for elephant
so gentle but strong

e is for ending
the show with a song!

F f

f is for farm
with fresh milk and cheese

f is for fingers
the toothpaste to squeeze

f is for fan
a cool breeze to make

f is for fish
that swim in the lake

G g

g is for grapes
some green, some black

g is for garbage
that's put in a sack

g is for garden
where flowers do grow

g is for galoshes
to wear in the snow

H h

h is for hedgehog
who cleans up the garden

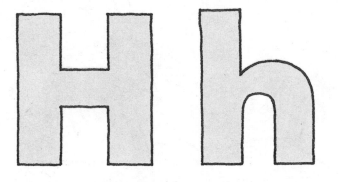

h is for hiccup
I beg your pardon!

h is for hymn
that is sung in a church

h is for hen
asleep on her perch

Ii

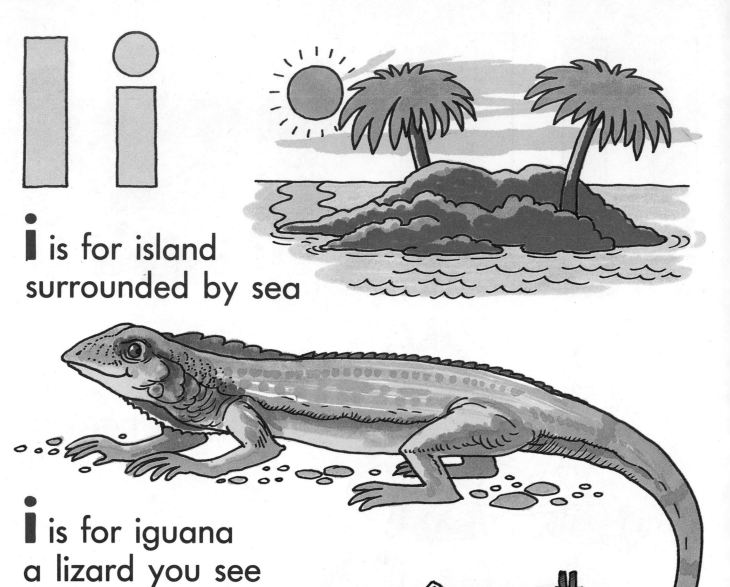

i is for island
surrounded by sea

i is for iguana
a lizard you see

i is for inn
a welcoming sight

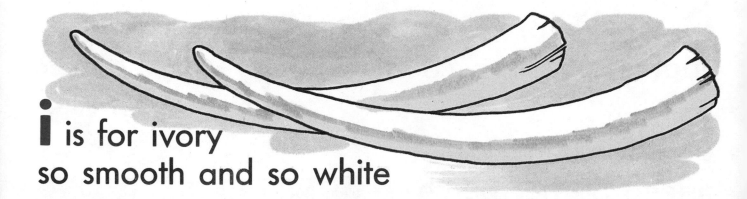

i is for ivory
so smooth and so white

J j

j is for jug
full of water so cool

j is for jumping
into the pool

j is for jam
to spread on your bread

STRAWBERRY JAM

j is for jet
that roars overhead

K k

k is for king
so stately and tall

k is for kitten
who plays with the ball

k is for kitchen
where cooking is done

k is for keeping
a secret, it's fun

L l

l is for lion
so noble and strong

l is for the lark
and merry birdsong

l is for leopard
known for his spots

l is for lemon
to squeeze lots and lots

M m

m is for mouse
who lives in a barn

m is for minstrel
who sings his own yarn

m is for mask
that hides your face

25miles

m is for marathon
a very long race

N n

n is for nurse
so patient with care

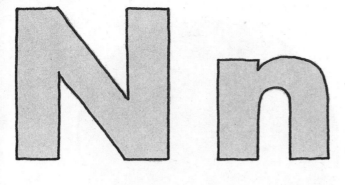

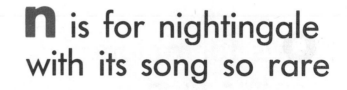

n is for nightingale
with its song so rare

n is for nut
so crunchy to eat

n is for navy
and ships in the fleet

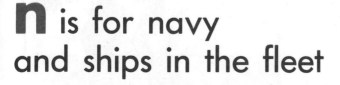

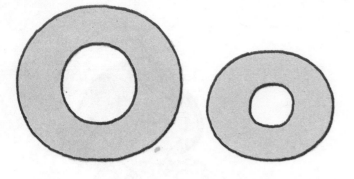

O is for orange
as round as a ball

O is for ostrich
with its neck so tall

O is for oblong
longer than a square

O is for orchid
a flower so rare

P p

p is for parrot
a beautiful bird

p is for pasture
and grazing a herd

p is for parachute
that floats to the ground

p is for pumpkin
oval or round

Qq

q is for quack
it's the way a duck talks

q is for queen
who smiles as she walks

q is for quilt
so warm yet so light

q is for quail
so pretty in flight

R r

r is for robin
with its bright red breast

r is for resting
like a bird in its nest

r is for roses
that grow down the lane

r is for rainbow
after the rain

S s

S is for sparrow
to the garden he comes

S is for starling
looking for crumbs

S is for snow
cold, crisp and white

S is for stars
that shine in the night

T t

t is for target
at which we take aim

t is for teddybear
he's good for a game

t is for ticket
to go see a play

t is for treat
a different one
each day

U u

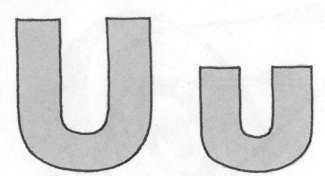

U is for universe
the planets and stars

U is for Uranus
a planet, like Mars

U is for uniforms
the guards in a row

U is for under
the arches we go!

V v

V is for vine
heavy with fruit

V is for valet
preparing a suit

V is for vikings
who sailed the high seas

V is for vegetables
potatoes, parsnips and peas

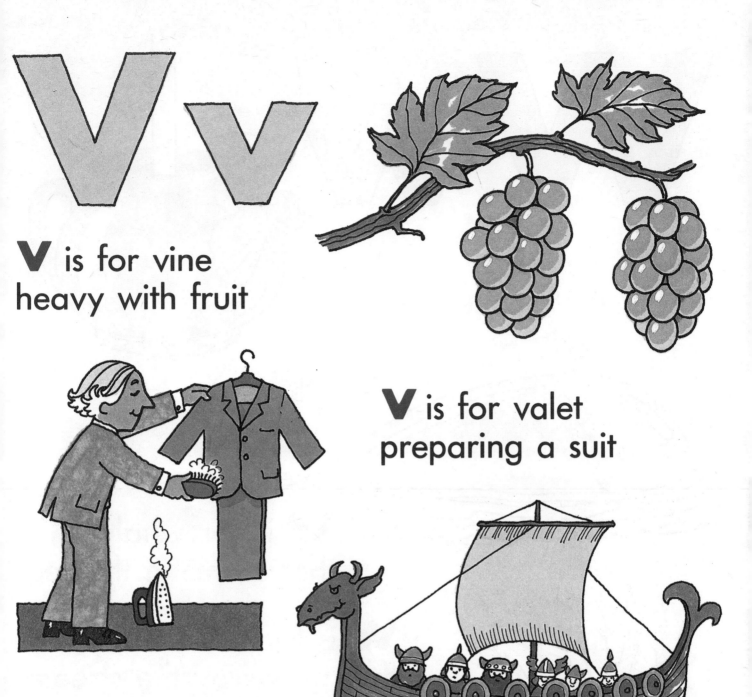

Ww

W is for water
we use to make tea

W is for whale
that swims in the sea

W is for the willow
that grows by the stream

W is for waking
from a beautiful dream

Xx

X is for x-rays
used in hospitals you know
they can see through you
from your head to your toe

X is for xylophone
an instrument to play

X is for ten
the old roman way

Y y

y is for yellow
and daffodils so pale

y is for yacht
under full sail

y is for yeast
that helps make bread dough

y is for yearling
a young horse you know

Z z

Z is for zebras
with their black and white coats

Z is for zither
playing musical notes

Z is for zoo
and the animals there

Z is for zig-zag
in a car beware

NOW YOU KNOW YOUR ABC's!

Here are some of the words you learned in this book. Can you match each word's first letter to a letter on the special alphabet quilt on the next page?
Say the letter as you find it.

a airplane
apples

b blanket
breakfast

c cars
cat

d dog

e eggs
elephant

f farm
fish

g garden
grapes

h hen
hymn

i island
ivory

j jet
jug

k king
kitchen

l lion
lemon

m mask
mouse

n navy
nurse

o oblong
orange

p parrot
pumpkin

q quilt

r rainbow
roses

s snow
stars

t teddybear
ticket

u uniforms

v vegetables

w water
whale

x x-rays
xylophone

y yellow

z zebras
zoo